Pedigree®

Published 2010.
Pedigree Books, Beech Hill House, Walnut Gardens, Exeter, Devon, EX4 4DH.
books@pedigreegroup.co.uk. www.pedigreebooks.com

Barbie™

Welcome to my brand new 2011 Winter Annual! The pages inside are bursting with fun fashions, make-its and pictures for you to colour and share with your best friends. I've written a host of puzzles and quizzes too, and this year there are two thrilling stories for you to read! If you want to find out about me and all things Barbie, you've come to the right place – have a super time!

Barbie x x x

£7.99

CHECK OUT THE

BarbiBuzz!

Hey girls! I thought you'd like the chance to learn more about me and my world, so why not explore these pages from BarbiBuzz? It's a fun website that Steven set up for me – he's a total techno-genius! Now even when we can't be together my friends and I are just a click away! On these next few pages you'll be able to read on our news, messages and photos, as well as finding out about our favourite things to do!

Barbie X

❀ **UPDATE** ☒

Barbie

Barbie is currently... having an amazing time shopping at the mall with Stacie!

❀ **FRIENDS**

Kelly   Ken

Nikki   Ryan

Stacie   Steven

Summer   Teresa

❀ **PERSONAL INFO** ☒

Height: 175cm
Eye colour: Blue
Hair: Long and golden blonde

Barbie is related to:
Stacie & Kelly (sisters)

Likes and interests:
Hanging with my friends
Playing guitar, piano and singing
My gorgeous animals Sequin, Lacey,
Blissa and Tawney.
Fashion – I'm a dedicated follower of style!

SEARCH

✿ MESSAGES

 Of course I'll be at your sleepover Barbie, Nikki and I can't wait. Shall I bring a movie? Love Teresa

 Hi Barbie, would love to come on Saturday but am at a tennis tournament. Back on the 25th. Shall we hook up then? Summer x

 Hi Sis, great profile pic! Love Stacie :)

 Barbie, can you make my gig next week? It should really rock! There are some other cool bands on the bill too. Ryan.

 See you at the beach barbeque on Sunday? Love Ken

✿ PHOTOS

Learning lines for my latest movie (with a little help from Lacey!)

Chill-axin' with Teresa

The gang at my place

✿ GROUPS

Barbie joined the groups 'Save the Dolphin' and 'I ♡ Poodles'

❀ UPDATE   X

Teresa

is currently...
at a ballet class

❀ FRIENDS

Barbie   Ken

Nikki   Ryan

Stacie   Steven

Summer   Kelly

❀ PERSONAL INFO   X

Height: 173cm

Eye colour: Hazel

Hair: Long, wavy and brown with red highlights

....

Teresa is related to: Nana Lana (grandmother)

....

Likes and interests:

I love giving stray animals a home

Baking – my Nana has taught me some

yummy recipes!

Dancing

Painting and drawing

✿ MESSAGES

Barbie

Hey Teresa, do you fancy coming over for a slumber party on Saturday night? I'm inviting all the girls. Love Barbie x

Ryan

Saw your new film Teresa. It's got Golden Globe written all over it!' Ryan

Nikki

Are you going to Barbie's place on Saturday? Shall I pick you up? Love Nikki

Summer

Missing you girlfriend! Am on a winning streak at the tournament, but the weather is awful – can't wait to get back to Malibu. Love Summer

✿ PHOTOS

Cooking up a storm!

Me and my BFF Barbie

✿ GROUPS

Teresa joined the groups 'Cupcakes for Kids Charity' and 'Friends of LA Animal Shelter'

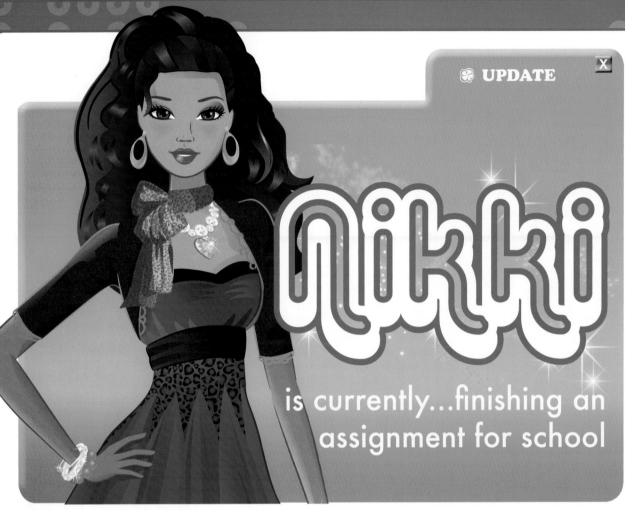

❀ **UPDATE**   X

nikki

is currently...finishing an assignment for school

❀ **FRIENDS**

Barbie

Ken

Teresa

Ryan

Raquelle

Steven

❀ **PERSONAL INFO**   X

Height: 173cm

Eye colour: Brown

Hair: Long and dark brown with golden highlights

....

Nikki is related to: Four sisters

....

Likes and interests:

I enjoy spinning tunes for my friends

Acting

Reading

Photography. I never go out without my digital camera.

❁ MESSAGES ✕

Steven

Nikki, did you upgrade to that cool new mobile phone we were talking about? Steven x

Summer

Hi Nix, are you up for a shop-a-thon next weekend? Love Raquelle

Barbie

So glad you can come to my sleepover! Got soooo much to talk about, lol Barbie xx

❁ PHOTOS ✕

Hanging at Barbie's with my girlz

Check out my cool new scarf. A total find!

❁ GROUPS ✕

Nikki joined the groups 'Malibu Photo Club' & 'Fashion Addicts Clothes Exchange'

UPDATE X

Summer

is currently...at a tennis tournament in Europe

FRIENDS

Barbie

Ken

Teresa

Ryan

Steven

PERSONAL INFO X

Height: 170cm
Eye colour: Green
Hair: Long and strawberry blonde

....

Summer is related to: Four brothers

....

Likes and interests:

I'm crazy about tennis – luckily it's my passion and my job

Hiking with my friends

Anything that gets my heart racing! White water rafting, triathlon, surfing...the list goes on and on

Barbie

Hi Summer, we're missing you a lot. Hurry home.
Love Barbie

Ken

Glad to hear you're playing well Summer, but think I'll give you a run for your money on the court when you get back. Have been doing a lot of cardio training with soccer and surfing so am super fit! See ya soon. Ken

Teresa

Thanx for your super-cool postcard! Miss you, Teresa x

❀ PHOTOS

Me doing what I do best!

Visiting Barbie behind-the-scenes of her latest movie set

❀ GROUPS

Summer joined the group 'Sports For All' and 'Xtreme Skydivers'

❀ UPDATE X

Raquelle

is currently...choosing an outfit for the pool party this weekend. I'm gonna look amazing!

❀ FRIENDS X

Barbie

Ken

Ryan

Nikki

Steven

❀ PERSONAL INFO X

Height: 178cm

Eye colour: Blue

Hair: Long, straight and raven

....

Raquelle is related to: Ryan (twin brother)

....

Likes and interests:

I love the spotlight – I was born to be in it. I feel happiest on the catwalk, showcasing my style
Rocking out to my twin Ryan's latest beats!
Designer Fashion

SEARCH

❋ **MESSAGES** X

Nikki

Hi Raquelle, saw you in that magazine fashion spread. The black dress looked amazing on you. Would definitely be up for shopping trip next week. Call me. Nikki x

Ryan

Hey Sis, you coming to the gig? Ry

Barbie

Just signed to make a movie in Paris! Maybe we can hook up at the catwalk shows? Barbie x

❋ **PHOTOS** X

Looking good at the latest première

Shopping trip with Nikki!

❋ **GROUPS** X

Raquelle joined the group 'Top Model Network'

❀ **UPDATE** X

Stacie

is currently...waiting for Barbie to come out of the fitting room so they can go for sodas!

❀ **FRIENDS**

Barbie
Kelly
Nikki
Summer
Teresa

❀ **PERSONAL INFO** X

Height: 137cm

Eye colour: Blue

Hair: Blonde, shoulder length

....

Stacie is related to: Barbie & Kelly (sisters)

....

Likes and interests:

I adore reading and making up my own stories. I might even write a book when I'm older!

Arts and crafts

All sports – baseball and basketball are fun, but I also do track and field

✿ MESSAGES X

Barbie

Hi Stacie, meet me at 11am at the entrance to the mall. Can't wait to check out that cool new shoe store!' Barbie xx

Kelly

I did go in your room because I wanted to borrow some sparkly hair clips. Sorry, I'll ask next time. Love from Kelly

Summer

Let's book another coaching session when I'm back from my tournament. Your tennis is getting really good! Summer

✿ PHOTOS X

Me with my sisters

Our beautiful kitten Blissa

✿ GROUPS X

Stacie joined the groups 'Creative Kidz' and 'California Junior Sports League'

❀ **UPDATE** ☒

kelly

is currently...playing in the garden

❀ **FRIENDS** ☒

Barbie   Stacie

Teresa

❀ **PERSONAL INFO** ☒

Height: **107cm**
Eye colour: **Blue**
Hair: **Sunny blonde, to my shoulders**

Kelly is related to: **Barbie & Stacie (sisters)**

Likes and interests:
Singing, dancing and acting
Riding my bike along the boardwalk at the beach
I love my family – especially my brilliant big
sister Barbie!

✿ MESSAGES

Barbie

Hi little Sis, so you're finally on BarbiBuzz! Don't forget we have a double audition on Thursday, I'll drop by later to run through lines with you. Love Barbie x

Stacie

Hey Kelly, have you been in my room again?!!!! Stacie

Teresa

I'm going to the petting zoo on Saturday, would you like to come too? Teresa

✿ PHOTOS

A trip to the candy shop with Barbie!

Putting on a show

✿ GROUPS

Kelly has not joined any groups

✿ UPDATE X

is currently...waxing my surfboard and hoping there's a good swell

✿ FRIENDS X

Barbie   Nikki

Teresa   Steven

Raquelle Summer

✿ PERSONAL INFO X

Height: 188cm
Eye colour: Blue
Hair: Blonde

....

Ken is related to: Two little brothers

....

Likes and interests:

Any sport – from soccer to surfing!
My favourite thing to do on the weekend
(besides hanging with my friends) is to be
up before dawn, heading down to the beach
to catch the first waves as the sun rises

✿ MESSAGES

Steven

Hey Ken, how's it going bro? Do you fancy coming over and trying out my new computer game later? Steven

Summer

Hi Ken, hope you've been practicing your serve, as I'm on fire at the moment. Am back in Malibu soon so it's going to be game on for our next match! Love Summer

Barbie

Definitely see you at the beach party Ken. It should be great. Barbie x

Raquelle

Long time no see Ken – when's the next soccer match? I may come along… if fashion week commitments permit. Raquelle x

✿ PHOTOS

Barbie and me at the prom

Chillin' at the café before science class

✿ GROUPS

Ken joined the groups 'Keep the beach clean' and Soccer Camp 2011'

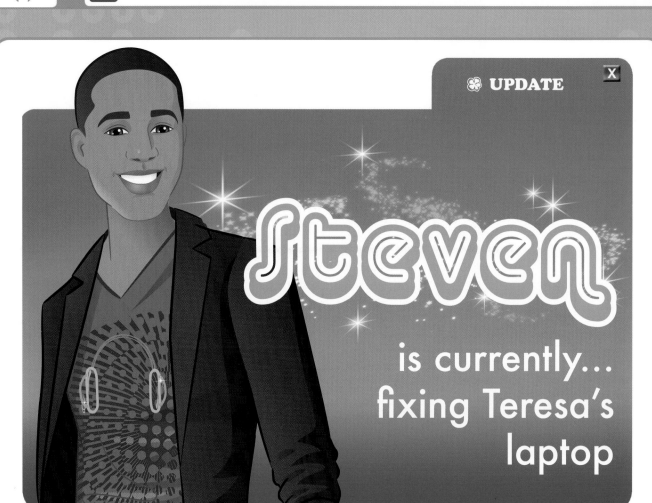

UPDATE ✿

Steven

is currently...
fixing Teresa's laptop

X

✿ FRIENDS

Barbie

Nikki

Teresa

Summer

Ken

Ryan

✿ PERSONAL INFO

X

Height: 183cm

Eye colour: Honey brown

Hair: Dark brown and cropped

....

Steven is related to: Two brothers & two sisters

....

Likes and interests:

I love anything with keys, switches and a screen!
Oh and the Web... what did people do before
the Internet?

Watching stand-up comedy shows

Karaoke sing-offs with my friends

❀ MESSAGES ☒

Teresa

Hey Steven, thanks so much for helping out with my computer. Let me know when I can pick it up and I'll take you out for lunch as a 'thank you'! Teresa x

Ken

Stevo! Where are you at man? Don't you ever look at your messages! Give me a call. Ken

Summer

I loved shooting hoops with you and Ken last week. Can't wait to catch up when I get back from Europe. Love Summer

❀ PHOTOS ☒

Me and my old pal Barbie

My revamped, hi-spec workstation. Great or what?!

❀ GROUPS ☒

Steven joined the group 'Best Comedy Lines of All Time'

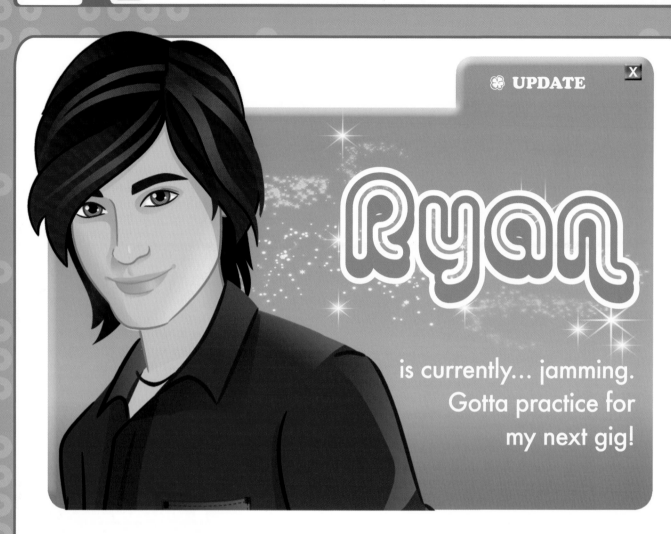

❁ **UPDATE** X

Ryan

is currently... jamming.
Gotta practice for
my next gig!

❁ **FRIENDS**

Barbie
Nikki
Teresa
Steven
Raquelle

❁ **PERSONAL INFO** X

Height: 190cm
Eye colour: Brown
Hair: Dark brown

....

Ryan is related to: Raquelle (twin sister)

....

Likes and interests:
Playing guitar
Writing both songs and poetry
– a poem is a song that just needs music!
Long walks along the beach
Camping under the stars

✿ MESSAGES ✕

Barbie

I've written some new song lyrics, will you tell me what you think? Text me when you've got an hour free, Barbie x

....

Raquelle

Ry, I would love to come to your gig – but only if you can make my fashion show – have saved you a front row seat. Raquelle

....

Teresa

Glad you liked my film. Not sure that I deserve an award just yet! Thanks for coming though, Teresa xx

✿ PHOTOS ✕

Just walkin' the dawg!

My guitar = my one true love

Rocking the stage at my last gig

✿ GROUPS ✕

Ryan joined the groups 'RockFest USA' and 'Young Songwriters Guild'

Kitty Crèche

Helping out at the vet's surgery is so much fun! Today I've been asked to look after this cat's gorgeous baby kittens – each one needs grooming, feeding and then putting on their blanket for a nap. The playful little kitties are having a game with me this morning! Can you count up how many are hiding in the surgery so I can scoop up each one and pop it into bed?

i can be...

I can find...
hiding kittens

Snowflake Chic

It's snowing outside my bedroom window! I'm going to pull on my clothes and then check out the winter wonderland that's waiting in the garden! Can you help me pick the right the outfit for the weather today? Colour in the snowflake next to the items that would work best on a crispy cold morning.

Late Date Maze

I'm going to a movie première with my two BFF this evening, but I'm running terribly late! Instead of waiting in a city traffic jam, I've decided to take a shortcut on foot. Can you help me find my way through the backstreets so that I make it to the movie theatre on time?

Start ▽

Finish ▶

Superstar Sisters

Both my little sisters are stars in my eyes! This is my favourite photo of Stacey and Kelly. It was taken on the last sunny day of autumn after a super day out at the Malibu funfair.

i can be... Dancing Queen

Musical Moves Wordsearch

There are so many wonderful ways to dance! I've hidden eight of my favourite dance styles somewhere in this word grid, see if you can find each and every one. The words might be running in any direction, so you'll need to look carefully.

D	I	S	C	O	X	Q	T
X	W	T	J	I	V	E	R
F	G	P	P	Y	G	J	M
L	T	A	S	E	A	P	O
A	E	T	D	N	S	T	O
M	E	D	E	I	U	V	R
E	R	F	K	L	Y	Z	L
N	T	S	G	J	L	Z	L
C	S	H	T	P	B	A	A
O	M	L	F	W	H	J	B

BALLROOM ☐ STREET ☐ TAP ☐

JAZZ ☐ LINE ☐ JIVE ☐

FLAMENCO ☐ DISCO ☐ BALLET ☐

30

Make Up Your Own Dance Routine!

Inventing a brand new dance routine is called choreography. Anyone can do it – all you need are a CD or MP3 player, lots of imagination and time to practice. Here's my simple guide for making up a routine packed with all sorts of graceful new moves.

First things first

Making up an impressive routine really is as easy as 1, 2, 3!

1. Pick a song that you love and then choose a dance style that fits. Maybe you'd like to do some ballet to a piece of classical music or a cool line-dance to a country and western song.

2. Find your dancers

Are you going to perform a solo number or would you prefer to plan out a stunning routine with a big troupe of friends?

3. Play your dance tune over and over again. Listen to the music. How does it make you feel? Does the intro start slowly or does it jump out of nowhere with a loud disco beat? When you know the song inside out, you're ready to match the moves to the music.

Top dancing tips

• Dancing requires flair and flexibility! Move your body with the rhythm of the music, changing moves in time to the beat.

• Surprise your audience. Don't be restricted by the dancing style you've chosen, the best routines include steps that are adventurous and unexpected.

• Be graceful at all times. Think how every part of your body will look on stage. Point your toes, extend your arms and hold your head up high.

• Learn it by heart. The best dancers never skimp on their rehearsal time. Practise your routine over and over again so that you're ready to put on a flawless performance.

Best Friends Forever

This quick quiz is a fabulous way to work out how well you know your closest pal! Grab a pencil then sit next to each other with one of these pages in front of you. Answer all of the questions as quickly as you can, trying not to look at your best friend's answers.

When you've finished, swap places then tot up your score.

1. What is your friend's favourite flavour of ice cream?

....

2. What colour are her eyes?

....

3. What is her favourite TV show?

....

4. What is her favourite animal?

....

5. Where did she last go on holiday?

....

6. What's the name of her oldest cuddly toy?

....

7. What's her favourite subject at school?

....

8. When did you and your friend first meet?

....

9. What's your friend's most prized possession?

....

10. What's her favourite hobby?

....

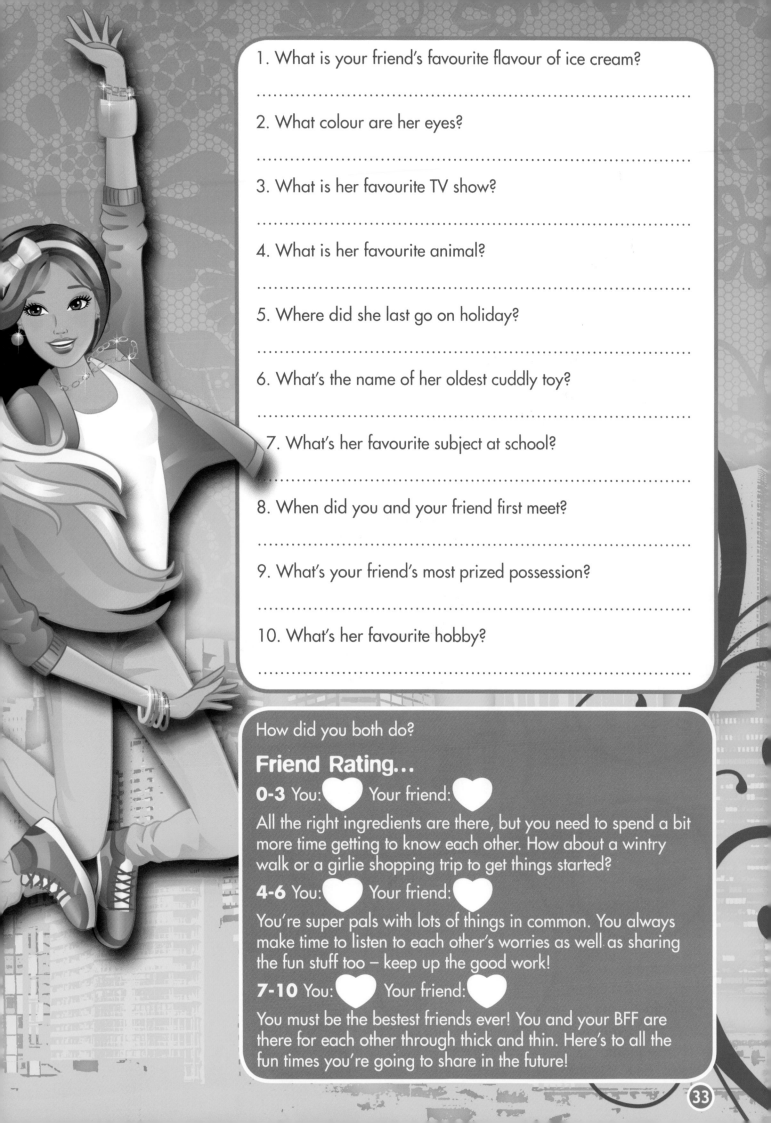

1. What is your friend's favourite flavour of ice cream?

....

2. What colour are her eyes?

....

3. What is her favourite TV show?

....

4. What is her favourite animal?

....

5. Where did she last go on holiday?

....

6. What's the name of her oldest cuddly toy?

....

7. What's her favourite subject at school?

....

8. When did you and your friend first meet?

....

9. What's your friend's most prized possession?

....

10. What's her favourite hobby?

....

How did you both do?

Friend Rating...

0-3 You: 🤍   Your friend: 🤍

All the right ingredients are there, but you need to spend a bit more time getting to know each other. How about a wintry walk or a girlie shopping trip to get things started?

4-6 You: 🤍   Your friend: 🤍

You're super pals with lots of things in common. You always make time to listen to each other's worries as well as sharing the fun stuff too – keep up the good work!

7-10 You: 🤍   Your friend: 🤍

You must be the bestest friends ever! You and your BFF are there for each other through thick and thin. Here's to all the fun times you're going to share in the future!

Perfect Pairs

My shoe closet has got into a terrible muddle! Can you help me sort out my sandals from my slingbacks? Draw a line between each matching pair so that I can pack them back on the rack.

Thank you so much! When you've finished, draw in a pair of shoes to go with my new jeans.

Design n' Decorate

Would you like to design a new outfit for me to wear to the Christmas prom? Join the dots to create a gorgeous ruched cocktail dress and then add any modifications you fancy. How about drawing in delicate off-the-shoulder sleeves or a pretty ribbon sash?

Colour the gown in, then decorate it with beads or sparkly jewels. Then I'm ready to dress up and go!

Barbie *i can be...* A Zoo Vet

Part 1

One beautiful sunny day, Isabella and Anna were playing outside in Anna's garden. The two little girls were best friends. Their favourite thing was to sit in the sunshine, making up new adventures for their Barbie dolls.

"Let's make up a story about Barbie and her friends at the zoo," smiled Anna.
    "Good idea!" cried Isabella. "Barbie can be a vet!"
"She can help take care of all the animals," Anna added excitedly.
    Both the girls clapped their hands. It was time to start the story…

…it was the first day of the summer holidays and Barbie, Teresa and Nikki were off to help look after the baby animals at the zoo.

"We've got the best volunteer jobs ever!" Barbie smiled, linking arms with Nikki and Teresa. She always loved trying new things with her friends.

When they reached the zoo gates, the vet in charge was already waiting for them.

"Thank goodness you're here," she said. "There are so many animals to look after. We really need your help."

The girls quickly changed into the uniforms the vet gave them, then clipped on their special access passes.

"We're ready," grinned Barbie, pulling on her pink boots.

The vet looked relieved. "Time to get started!"

The friends set off down the path, turning right at the zoo's ticket office.

As they walked along the vet explained what their duties would be.

"It's your job to make sure that the baby animals and birds are happy and safe," she said. "There's a long list of jobs to do. The most important thing is to keep their food and water topped up regularly."

"No problem," smiled Barbie.

The vet suggested that the girls use bikes with pink trailers to carry the animals' food all around the zoo. Barbie felt her heart flutter with excitement! Before they began their rounds, there was just time to ask the vet about her job.

"A vet takes care of animals and birds if they get sick or hurt. I also give check-ups to all the zoo's healthy animals," the vet explained.

Barbie watched as the vet carefully wrote some notes on a sheet of paper.

"Here's a list of all the birds and baby animals that you need to feed," she added. "Can you do it?"

"Sure we can!" Nikki replied confidently.

"You'll have to work fast," the vet warned, pointing the way to the baby koalas. When the girls arrived at the koala's enclosure, a tiny bear ran up to Barbie and twitched his nose.

"I think he likes your perfume!" laughed Teresa.

"Hello cutie," Barbie giggled, stroking the fluffy youngster.

One by one, the koalas scampered up to drink their milk. It didn't take them long to finish every drop!

"Look at those ones playing on the swing!" Teresa laughed, tidying up the empty bottles.

Barbie and Nikki went over to the swing and gently pushed the little koalas. "This is fun!" said Barbie. "Let's stay here and play for a while."

After they'd finished playing with the koalas, the girls headed to the safari enclosure.

"Where are all the animals?" said Nikki, as they hopped off their bikes.

Barbie pointed to some tracks on the ground. The friends followed the marks to a waterhole where several stunning baby animals were gathered.

Just as they finished feeding them, a group of visitors drove up in a tour bus. "Would you pose for some pictures?" asked a lady. "It would be wonderful to take some photos of three vets at work."

The girls were more than happy to pose with the lovable little animals.

"It's fun being a zoo vet," giggled Barbie, as she Nikki and Teresa finally set off to feed the dolphins. As soon as they got close to the pool, the friendly creatures started clapping their fins.

"I think they want us to throw some fish," grinned Teresa.

The dolphins jumped and twirled as they caught the fish that the girls threw them.

Barbie couldn't help but giggle. "Now that's what I call fast food!"

It was time to go on to the elephants, but none of the friends could resist a few more minutes' water play. Soon all the dolphins were playing beach ball with the girls.

Barbie, Teresa and Nikki spent a long time playing with the dolphins before finally riding their bikes over to the elephant enclosure.

"Would you like a nice drink?" asked Nikki, holding out a bucket to the tiniest grey elephant. The baby elephant dipped his trunk into the bucket and sucked up some water. Suddenly he sent a spray of water splashing over all over Nikki! Barbie and Teresa burst out laughing, and a moment later, Nikki joined in too.

"I wish I had a camera!" grinned Barbie.

Nikki pushed her hair back with one hand, sighing "I wish I had a hairdryer!"

The BFFs were giggling so much at Nikki's drenching, they didn't notice the cheeky elephant dipping his trunk back into the bucket all over again.

"Watch out, guys!" yelled Nikki, pointing over Barbie and Teresa's shoulder. The friends started to run, but it was too late! The naughty little elephant let out a fountain of water and soaked them too!

"That's a pretty unusual way to take a shower!" giggled Barbie, as everyone burst out laughing.

The three friends sat down on some rocks to dry out in the sun. Suddenly, Barbie jumped to her feet. She put her hand in her pocket and pulled out the list of jobs that the vet had given her.

"Oh, no!" she cried. "We forgot about the list! We still have lots of baby animals to feed. We shouldn't have spent so long playing and posing for pictures." Teresa pulled out her mobile phone so they could check the time.

"It's getting late already," she frowned.
The girls looked at each other in horror. They'd been having so much fun they'd completely forgotten that they had a very important job to do!

Will Barbie and her friends be able to get all the animals fed and watered before bedtime?
Turn to page 88 to find out!

Mmm Mamma Mia!

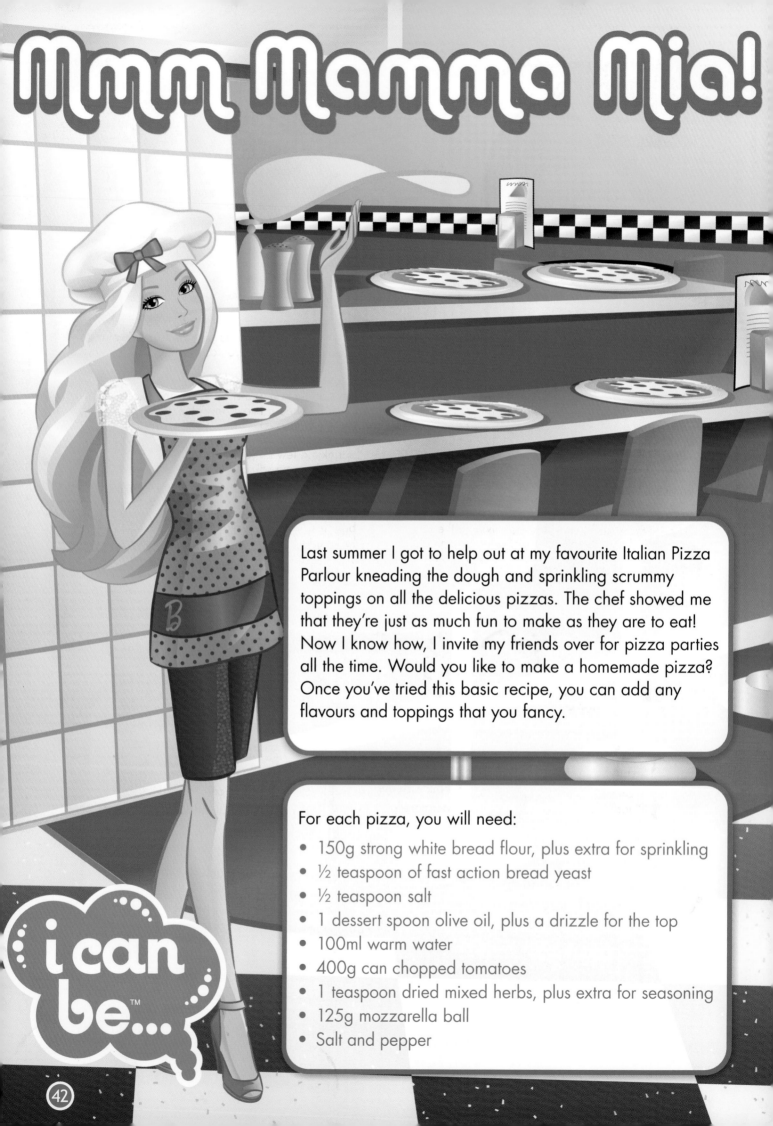

Last summer I got to help out at my favourite Italian Pizza Parlour kneading the dough and sprinkling scrummy toppings on all the delicious pizzas. The chef showed me that they're just as much fun to make as they are to eat! Now I know how, I invite my friends over for pizza parties all the time. Would you like to make a homemade pizza? Once you've tried this basic recipe, you can add any flavours and toppings that you fancy.

For each pizza, you will need:

- 150g strong white bread flour, plus extra for sprinkling
- ½ teaspoon of fast action bread yeast
- ½ teaspoon salt
- 1 dessert spoon olive oil, plus a drizzle for the top
- 100ml warm water
- 400g can chopped tomatoes
- 1 teaspoon dried mixed herbs, plus extra for seasoning
- 125g mozzarella ball
- Salt and pepper

i can be...

PIZZA

Always ask an adult to help you before starting any cookery projects.

1. Ask a grown-up to turn the oven onto 220°C/425°F/Gas Mark 7.

2. Tip the flour into a mixing bowl, then stir in the yeast and salt.

3. Use a spoon to make a hole in the middle of the mixture, then slowly pour in the olive oil and warm water. Stir everything together until it forms a pale dough.

4. Sprinkle some more flour on a clean, dry worktop then place the pizza dough in the middle. Knead the dough for a few minutes with your hands, turning it all the time so that it doesn't stick to the surface. Don't be afraid to dust the counter with more flour if you need to!

5. Once the dough is nice and soft, put it on a plate and cover it up with a tea towel while you prepare the tomato sauce.

6. Ask your helper to open the can of tomatoes and pour them into a non-stick pan. Mix in the spoonful of herbs, then heat the mixture up until it boils down into a thick red sauce. Keep stirring the tomatoes so that they don't catch on the base of the pan, then turn the heat off so that the sauce can cool.

7. Lift the tea towel off the dough, then sprinkle some more flour across the work surface. Use a rolling pin to roll the dough into a nice round shape about the size of a large dinner plate.

8. Shake another layer of flour onto your baking tray, then carefully transfer your dough on to it.

9. Use a wooden spoon to spread a thick layer of tomato sauce onto the pizza base, going as close to the edge as you can.

10. Snip open the packet containing the mozzarella ball and drain away the excess milk. Slice the cheese into rounds, then arrange it on top of your pizza.

11. Sprinkle a few more herbs on top, add some salt and pepper, then your pizza is ready to cook! Pop it in the oven for 8 to 10 minutes until the cheese bubbles and the dough looks crispy.

TOPPING SHOP

Hawaiian
Ham
Pineapple

Quattro Formaggi (Four Cheese)
Mozzarella
Ricotta cheese
Fontina cheese
Gorgonzola cheese

Meat feast
Pepperoni
Ham
Cooked bacon

Vegetarian
Red onions
Peppers
Sweetcorn
Mushrooms

Four seasons*
1. Plain tomato and mozzarella
2. Mushrooms
3. Anchovies and olives
4. Pepperoni

* To make this delicious pizza, separate your toppings into four quarters:

Pit Stop Problem

I believe that you can be anything that you want to be. Today, I'm imagining what it would be like to be a racing driver, roaring down the track in my own pink car!

Something doesn't seem quite right with these photos of me at the grand prix. While I take a pit stop, study the page closely. Can you spot six differences between the two scenes? Colour in a trophy for every one that you find.

Cheerleading Crossword

Cheerleading is such a blast! We learn fast routines, wave pom poms and sing for our high school team. If you'd like to learn more about this super-fun hobby, try and crack my cheerleading crossword. Good luck!

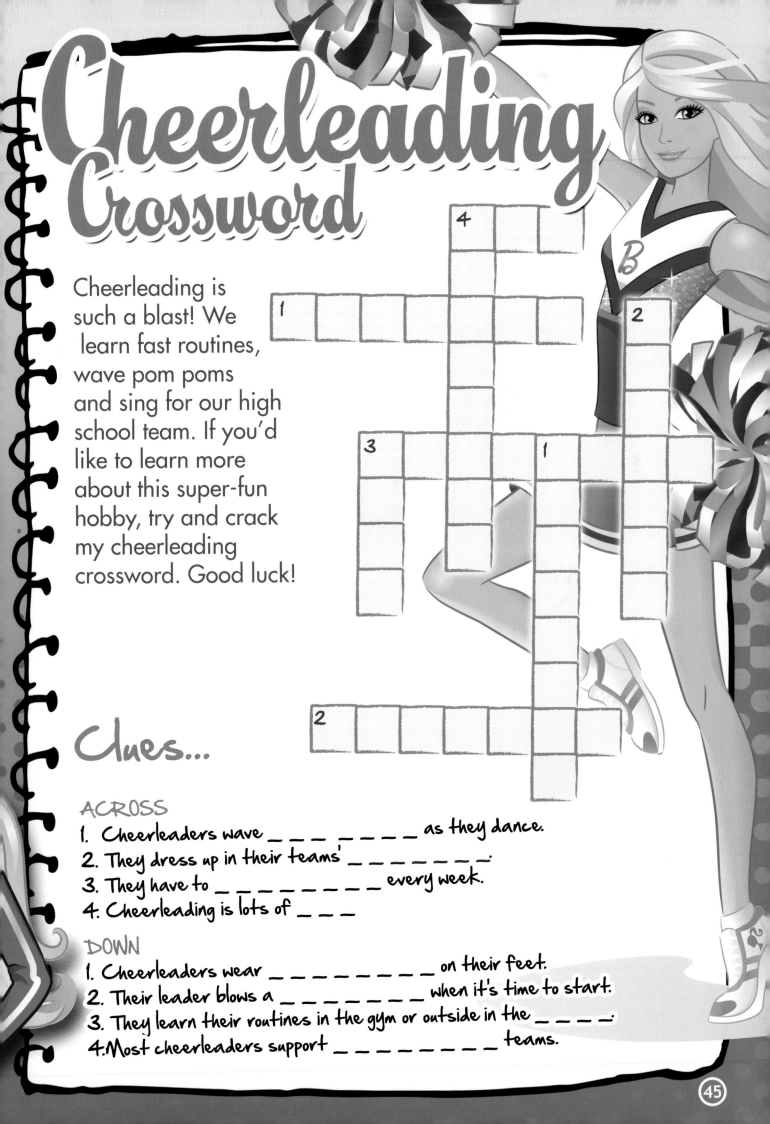

Clues...

ACROSS
1. Cheerleaders wave _ _ _ _ _ _ _ _ as they dance.
2. They dress up in their teams' _ _ _ _ _ _ _ _ _.
3. They have to _ _ _ _ _ _ _ _ _ every week.
4. Cheerleading is lots of _ _ _

DOWN
1. Cheerleaders wear _ _ _ _ _ _ _ _ _ _ on their feet.
2. Their leader blows a _ _ _ _ _ _ _ _ when it's time to start.
3. They learn their routines in the gym or outside in the _ _ _ _.
4. Most cheerleaders support _ _ _ _ _ _ _ _ teams.

My Secret Diary

Would you like a sneak peek inside my secret journal? To find out all my news, use the picture clues to help you fill the blanks with the right words.

Dear Diary,

What a busy day it has been! I was woken up first thing by the sound of the 📞 _ _ _ _ _ ringing. It was 👩 _ _ _ _ _ _ calling to say that the ☀ _ _ _ was shining! She asked if the whole gang could come over to my 🏠 _ _ _ _ _ for a swim in the 🏊 _ _ _ _, so of course I said yes!

👨 _ _ _ _ _ _ and 👱 _ _ _ arrived first, closely followed by 👩 _ _ _ _ _, 👩 _ _ _ _ and 👩 _ _ _ _ _ _ _ _. 👩 _ _ _ _ _ _ came last armed with a big box of her homemade 🧁 _ _ _ _ _ _ _ _.

We had so many laughs playing in the 🏊 _ _ _ _. When we couldn't splash anymore, we hung out eating 🧁 _ _ _ _ _ _ _ _ _. At three, 👱 _ _ _ turned my flatscreen 📺 _ _ on just in time to watch 👱 _ _ _ _ _ _ win her tennis tournament!

After everyone had left, I chilled out in my 🛏 _ _ _ _ _ _ _ with 🐶 _ _ _ _ _ _ and 🐰 _ _ _ _ _. What a lucky girl I am to be 👱 _ _ _ _ _ !

Barbie X X X

Finding it tricky? Don't forget that there are answers to help you at the back of the Annual.

Shopping Surprises

Nikki, Teresa and I are heading out for a dreamy day at the mall! We've each been saving up for a luxe new item that's on display in our favourite boutique. Follow the thought bubbles to find out what we're each going to buy, then draw a picture of it on each of our shiny shopping bags.

Stunning Shoebox Theatre

Have you ever peeped inside a shoebox theatre? It's the most magical thing in the world! Although it might look like a plain old shoebox on the outside, the inside has been transformed into a miniature stage complete with 3D puppets and props! These pages will show you how to make a tiny concert hall complete with curtains and pirouetting ballerinas. All you need are a few craft supplies, some patience and your imagination...

Making your theatre

You will need:
- A standard shoebox
- A large round coin
- A pencil
- Scissors
- Old newspaper
- Poster paint
- Paintbrush
- Tracing paper
- Paper glue

BE SCISSOR SAFE!
Ask an adult to help you with the cutting stages.

1. Turn your shoebox to the side, then put the coin where you would like your peep hole to go. Draw round the coin with a pencil, then lift it off and ask a grown-up to carefully cut out the hole.

2. Put the coin on the lid of the box and draw round it three times – creating three circles at even distances along the top. Ask your helper to cut these out too. These holes will allow light to shine on to your stage.

3. Now your shoebox is fitted with its viewing and light holes, place it on an old sheet of newspaper. Use poster paint to paint the inside base of the box in a bright orange and the sides in Barbie pink. Paint the inside lid of the box pink too, then give it time to dry.

4. Carefully trace or photocopy the theatre background from the facing page, cutting it down so that it is narrow enough to fit into the back of your box. Don't worry if the stage is too long for the shoebox, it should curve around the corners slightly to make the scene seem bigger.

5. Before you stick the background into the box, carefully trace the ballet dancers and set from page 50 onto a sheet of tracing paper. Put them to one side.

6. Run paper glue along each of the side edges of the background, then stick it inside the shoebox.

7. Now it's time to create your ballet scene! Turn to page 51 to find out what to do next...

Be Scissor Safe!
Ask an adult to help you
with the cutting
stages.

Stunning Shoebox Theatre

PART TWO

For this part, you will need:

- Thick white card
- Felt-tipped pens
- Glitter

1. Take your tracings from page 50 and 51 and carefully transfer each one onto a sheet of white card. Ask your helper to cut each piece out as accurately as they can.

2. Use your felt-tips to bring each ballerina to life. Make the tiaras, bodices and ballet shoes as beautiful as you can.

3. Dot the characters with glue, then place them on an old sheet of newspaper. Gently dust each with glitter, shake off any excess.

4. Use a bold pen to shade both curtains in the perfect shade of pink.

5. Take the rectangular templates that you cut out from the card and fold each one in half. Glue the upright half on the back of each character and at the top of the curtains.

6. You're ready to assemble your theatre! Use the tabs to stick each of the ballerinas onto the base of the stage, taking care to place them near the point where each light hole will shine. Next glue the top of each curtain to the lid of the shoe box, about 5cm in front of the backdrop.

7. Put the lid on your shoebox, play some heavenly music, then ask some special friends to peep inside. It's magic!

Did you know?

You can make shoebox theatres for any kind of theme you like. How about testing your drawing skills by trying one of these suggestions?

- Fairyland
- Catwalk
- A day at the zoo

Mystery Meeting!

I'm heading out for a wintry weekend snowball fight! Any ideas who I'm going to meet? Answer the chilly clues at the bottom of the page, then fill up the letter grid. When you're finished, the person's name will be running down the column in pink.

1. On cold mornings, it makes your garden sparkle.
2. Clear, sparkly gemstones that reflect rainbow colours.
3. Shoes to help you glide across the ice.
4. A winter accessory to keep your fingers warm.
5. A Christmassy animal with antlers.
6. A beautiful, tiny piece of snow.

I'm going out to see  !

Ten Top Ways to... Revamp Your Style

Are you in need of a fashion makeover? Every Autumn I go through my closet and sort through the clothes that I still love and the ones that it's time to recycle! I also take a little time out for pampering so that I'm ready for the party season.

Here's ten quick tips for refreshing your fashion favourites and giving yourself a beauty boost too:

1. Start by dividing your outfits into three piles – Pass On, Treasure Forever and Revamp. Be strict, anything that you've grown out of or haven't worn since last Christmas should be passed on for another girl to enjoy!

2. Give your Pass On collection to friends or the charity shop, then check that your Treasure Forever items don't need any taking care of. Now's the time to sew on buttons, cut away loose threads and wash off any little blemishes.

3. Lay your Revamp clothes on the table, think how you can give them another lease of life. Try pinning on badges, stitching on trims or adding designs in fabric paints.

4. Re-hang your honed down clothes collection by colour – that way you can see straight away what items go together.

5. Now take time to sort through your accessories. Any worn or holey socks and tights should go or be repaired. Try on all your shoes, only keeping the ones that really do fit! Empty your bags, giving dusty ones a wash down.

6. Get to work on your jewellery box! Untangle and unclip any knotted necklaces and chains, then hunt down missing earrings. Make space for your hair clips and brooches too, pinning them onto a piece of ribbon so that you can see them all easily.

7. When your outfits are looking freshened up and ready-to-wear, it's time to give yourself some special attention! Treat yourself to a bubbly bath, put on a facepack and condition your hair.

8. Ask a friend to take turns doing home manicures. Wipe away any old polish, then file your nails into soft round domes. Top each one off with a slick of clear nail varnish. It will look pretty and protect them too.

9. Make-up should be kept to a minimum – you're beautiful as you are! Take a little time too sort through your lipglosses, eye cream and glitter, making sure that you give away any that you've never worn. Leaky make-up should be taken out too.

10. Top off your Autumn revamp by striking a model pose. Put your shoulders back and lift your head up high – simply beautiful!

Barbie™
A Fashion Fairytale

Barbie discovers a magical secret...
And her inner sparkle!

Aunt Millicent

Marie-Alecia

Jacqueline

Delphine

Barbie gazed out of the aeroplane window to see the Eiffel Tower bathed in sunlight below. "Paris!" she breathed, turning to smile at her poodle Sequin. It had not been the best of days. First Todd, a hot-headed director, had asked her to leave the set of her latest movie when another actress suggested Barbie would do a better directing job. Then unbelievably, Ken had also broken up with her – by phone. Needing a break, Barbie had jumped on the first plane out of town. She was off to see her Aunt Millicent, a celebrated fashion designer.

When the flight landed Barbie and Sequin took a taxi to Millicent's fashion house. "Hello?" Barbie called, pushing the door open. The last time she'd visited this place had been a bustling showroom full of style and energy. Now it was a gloomy space filled with boxes. "Barbie!" cried a friendly voice. Aunt Millicent emerged, along with a pretty girl wearing glasses. Millicent tried to embrace her niece. Unfortunately the bright pink roller skates she was wearing sent her slamming straight into Barbie instead!

"I knew we'd have fun with you here!" laughed Millicent, pulling herself to her feet. "Marie-Alecia, this is my niece, Barbie. Barbie, this is Marie-Alecia. We call her Alice." The girls smiled and shook hands. "What's with the rippin' power pink roller skates?" Barbie asked her aunt. "They're contenders for my new hobby," replied Millicent. "I didn't want to tell you on the phone, but I'm shutting shop and moving to the country."

Barbie gasped as Millicent explained how the press had called her new fashion lines 'dated and washed-up'. She couldn't understand it, her aunt was so talented. Things became clearer when Alice told Barbie how a neighbouring designer called Jacqueline had copied Millicent's designs. Jacqueline was now the darling of the fashion press, promoting the outfits as her own work. "Millicent's had to sell this place to a hotdog chain," sighed Alice, leading Barbie up to the design studio on the second floor.

As they passed the first floor Sequin caught the eye of Millicent's Jack Russell Terrier, Jacques Rousseau. For years the little dog had spent every moment with Millicent, picking up her unique taent for style. "My new muse!" Jacques woofed to the pretty poodle. "Ze new inspirtion for my fashion genius!" Millicent's cat Jilliana shook her head in disgust.

When Barbie and Alice got to the second floor room, it was in a sorry, half-packed state. "Wow,"sighed Barbie. "This studio… I just remember it being so alive and magical." Alice nodded and excitedly dragged Barbie upstairs to the attic. The fashionista quickly spotted a beautiful pink dress hanging on a mannequin. "They were so wrong about Aunt Millicent's designs!" she frowned. "This dress is totally Vogue-worthy!" Shyly, Alice admitted she'd designed the dress herself. Suddenly she tugged at a dust cover, revealing a majestic wardrobe. Then she pulled out an old book with a picture of the same closet! "I've found stories of magic in here," she whispered. "Tales of mystical creatures who appeared from inside an ancient wardrobe."

"The book says that we can summon magical beings in two steps," Alice continued, telling Barbie that they must put a worthy design into the wardrobe and then find a chant written somewhere on the wall. Barbie put the dress Alice had made into the closet, then the pair scanned the walls. After a few moments, Barbie noticed an old handle. When she pulled it a metal plaque was revealed. Un, deux et trois! Et puis voila! La magic qui brille a chaque fois!

The girls read the words and magic lights began to swirl inside the wardrobe. Suddenly the doors burst open to reveal three tiny beings striking glamorous poses. "It's the magical creatures!" gasped Alice. "We are not creatures," said one. "We're Shyne, Shimmer and Glimmer." "You're fairies?" asked Barbie. "Observe," said Shyne. "No wings." "We're Flairies," explained Glimmer, waving her tiny arms. "We have flair." "A flair we share!" chirped Shimmer.

Alice and Barbie listened as the Flairies explained their calling – to help worthy designers find their va va voom. "We add shimmer, glimmer and shine," smiled Shyne. They also told the girls that this very building – constructed on the site of Paris' first fashion house – was the source of their power. If it became a hotdog joint the Flairies would be history.We need to see the lady in charge!" cried Shyne, taking off in a cascade of Flairydust. The girls followed the tiny trio downstairs to find Millicent, carrying Alice's glitterized gown.

It was no use. When the old lady had got over her surprise, she was adamant that there was nothing to be done. "It would cost a fortune to get out of the sale!" she cried. "I'd have to sell a whole new fashion line by Friday to make that kind of money. People don't like my work anymore. I'm sorry!" Suddenly a chic shopper burst into the store. "I must have that dress!" she cooed. "I'll pay anything you want." Barbie took Alice to one side. "Aunt Millicent says she can't make and sell a fashion line by Friday… but you can!"

Alice was unsure of her abilities, but Barbie and the Flairies were certain that her collection could save Millicent. "You can do this!" urged Barbie "We'll move the Flairies' Gliterizer closet into the studio and surround you with inspiration!" Barbie and Alice cruised the streets of Paris, looking for ideas.

Back in the studio Alice made sketches and began bringing the designs to life. Whenever a dress was finished the Flairies worked their magic to glitterize it. Soon the design studio was buzzing with energy again! Meanwhile back in LA, Barbie's friend Teresa discovered Ken hadn't really broken up with Barbie at all! Raquelle had tricked Ken by asking him to read lines from a script, which she'd recorded and played down the phone to Barbie. "I've got to make things right!" Ken told Teresa. "I'll book the next flight to Paris!"

Millicent was thrilled to see the studio turned back into a creative working space. She gave the girls the go ahead to put on their show, although she turned down the opportunity to design some clothes for the collection. "You've tried so hard," she said sadly. "The last thing you need is my reputation bringing you down."

Up on the first floor Jacques had been working just as hard to create a collection for pets. When Barbie and Alice saw Sequin decked out in one of Jacques' fantastic outfits they called in the Flairies to add a final touch. "That is one crazily cutting-edge canine," remarked Shyne. "Now we have two designers for the fashion show!" smiled Barbie, hanging Jacques' designs in the window alongside Alice's. The team were so busy, they didn't notice the snoops peering into the shop window. Thieving designer Jacqueline and her assistant Delphine had spotted the Flairies at work.

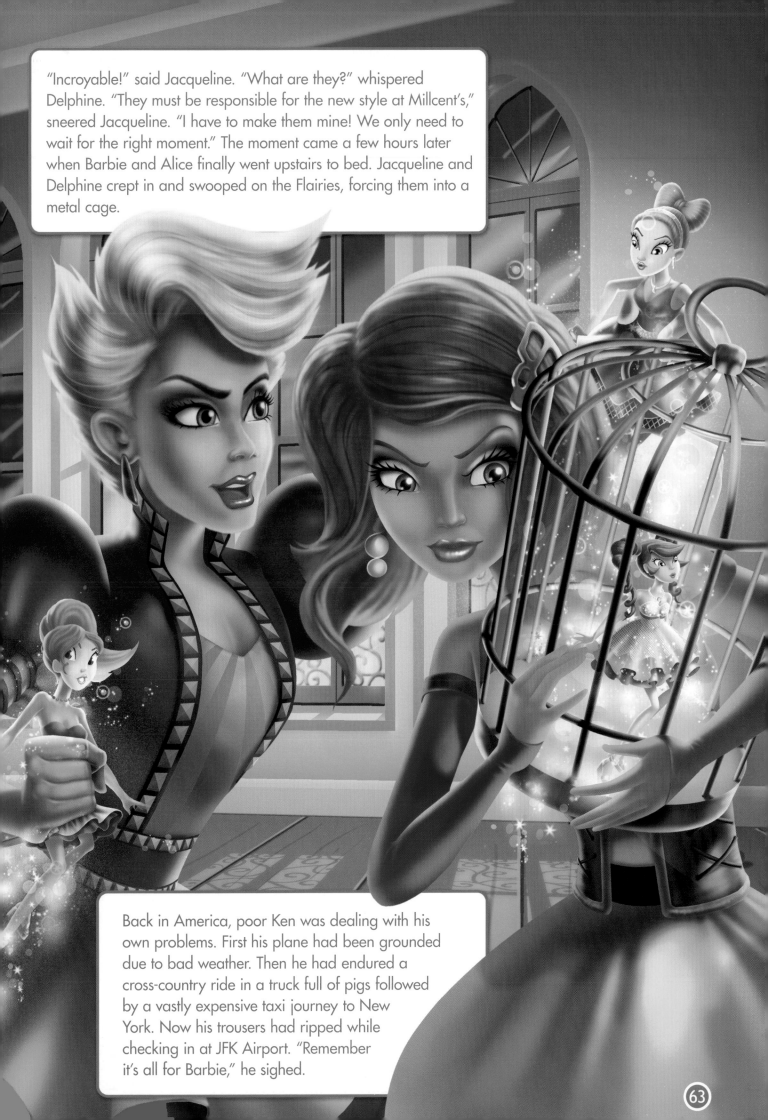

"Incroyable!" said Jacqueline. "What are they?" whispered Delphine. "They must be responsible for the new style at Millcent's," sneered Jacqueline. "I have to make them mine! We only need to wait for the right moment." The moment came a few hours later when Barbie and Alice finally went upstairs to bed. Jacqueline and Delphine crept in and swooped on the Flairies, forcing them into a metal cage.

Back in America, poor Ken was dealing with his own problems. First his plane had been grounded due to bad weather. Then he had endured a cross-country ride in a truck full of pigs followed by a vastly expensive taxi journey to New York. Now his trousers had ripped while checking in at JFK Airport. "Remember it's all for Barbie," he sighed.

The Flairy-nappers took their captives down to the basement in Jacqueline's fashion house. "You have no idea who you're dealing with!" shrieked Shyne. She attacked the cage with a tiny karate kick, but the bars were solid. "I'll let you out at some point," smirked Jacqueline "But not until you help me glitterize my designs so they look like the ones at Millicent's. The show I'm going to put on has got to outshine hers." The Flairies had no choice but to do as they were told, even though Jacqueline's work was terrible. With Millicent no longer around to copy, her rival was clearly lost. "Here's the deal," snapped Shyne.

"We're not inspired by these dresses. If we use our magic, we don't know what'll happen." There was a swirl of Flairydust as the trio transformed the designs into fantastic creations. "They're beautiful now," warned Glimmer. "But the magic is not stable."

The next morning, Barbie and Alice looked everywhere for the Flairies. "They can't be gone," fretted Barbie. "Why would they leave when we're trying to save their powers?" Alice was panicking too, but Millicent seemed speechless. "You designed all these outfits, even though people might say horrible things about your work?" she finally gasped. "It still might not be enough to save the fashion house." "I had to try," said Alice. "Not that it matters. The designs need the Flairies' help and they're gone."

Aunt Millicent smiled. "I don't have glitterizing powers," she nodded. "But maybe there's something I can do." Alice and Barbie beamed at the old lady. "I'm newly inspired by you," continued Millicent. "You're brave enough to follow your passion no matter what people might say. That is true style. It would be a dream come true to design with you!" laughed Alice. The delighted threesome agreed to work together to get the collection ready in time. Sequin and Jacques barked – even they were up for the challenge!

The whole team worked late into the evening to finish the collection. It was gone midnight when they finally fell asleep in the design studio amid a sea of fabulous frocks.

An hour later, flashing lights at the window woke Sequin up. The poodle nudged Jacques and Jilliana awake. Together they peered out to see where the lights were coming from. Across the street, fireworks were shooting up from the basement of Jacqueline's studio. "The Flairies!" barked Sequin. "She stole them!" woofed Jacques. "Meow!" screeched Jilliana. "It's up to us to get them back!" The quick-witted kitty padded out of the studio, slipping into Jacqueline's through a basement window.

The pets and the Flairies wasted no time in getting out of Jacqueline's and back over to Millicent's. The shimmering threesome got straight to work glitterizing the stunning new collection. Early next morning an exhausted Ken finally landed at Charles de Gaulle Airport in Paris. "Yes! I did it!" he shouted, falling to his knees and kissing the ground. Ken looked up to see a taxi cab pulling over. "Please take me to Millicent's Fashion House," he cried. The driver put his foot down on the accelerator. "C'est parti!"

Within minutes Jilliana had opened the door to allow Jacques and Sequin into Jacqueline's building. She quickly released the Flairies from their cage, using her claws as keys. "Beauty, brains and brawn," beamed Shyne as Glimmer and Shimmer hugged the clever puss. "Now that's stylish."

When Millicent, Alice and Barbie woke up, the Fashion House had been transformed. Every gown was now eye-poppingly gorgeous! The first floor had been magically decked out for a fashion show with a curtained stage and cool catwalk. "You came back!" Alice beamed at Shyne, Shimmer and Glimmer. "Those designs were perfect," smiled Shimmer. "We just sparkled them a little bit," Barbie cheered.

"We are so saving this place!" But by 8 o' clock that evening the room was still empty – the only people there were a photographer snapping an embarrassingly empty catwalk and the guy from the hotdog company. "You really think you can make enough money tonight to keep me from tearing this place down?" he crooned. The team looked on gloomily from behind the curtain. "I don't understand," frowned Barbie. "Where is everyone?" "People will come, I have faith. The two of you gave that to me," insisted Millicent.

At first it seemed to be business as usual over at Jacqueline's. The sneak had spent a fortune publicising her show and calling in favours from the press. Now the studio was packed with the biggest names in fashion. "It's the night of my dreams," she told Delphine. "Even Lilliana Roxelle is here, the most famous critic in France! Once I show these dresses I will be forever known as the best designer in all Paris!" This time however, her arrogance wasn't going to pay off. At first the audience 'oohed' and 'aahed' as the sparkling frocks swished down the catwalk.

But just as the Flairies had predicted, with uninspiring designs the magic couldn't hold and soon the dresses were back to garbage. "I've heard of trashy clothes, but this is ridiculous," moaned one guest as she rushed to join the throng heading out the door towards the bright lights of Millicent's. Jacqueline fell to the floor, begging for everyone to return.

"The whole room has suddenly got packed!' gasped Barbie, minutes later. Lilliana Roxelle was there in the front row, sneering down her nose at the hotdog guy. Now that the crowds were queuing out of the door, Millicent and Alice were both overwhelmed with nerves. "I know how hard it is to believe in yourself when it seems like the world is against you, but that's what you've both done," said Barbie. "Look at the results." "It's magical," said Alice. "When you believe in yourself, magic happens," nodded Millicent.
The threesome hugged.

"Let's rock this party!" laughed Barbie, sashaying through the curtains in one of Alice's most fabulous evening dresses. "We call this collection 'A Fashion Fairytale'," announced Millicent as Barbie, Sequin and Jilliana strutted their stuff in a succession of incredible outfits. "How about we finish this off with a bang?" suggested Glimmer when Barbie showed off the final dress. The Flairies appeared on the catwalk in front of the amazed audience. Their stunning presence added so much sparkle that the dress became dazzling in its beauty.

As Barbie took in the applause, the front door of Millicent's suddenly burst open. A familiar voice sailed across the whistles and cheers. "Barbie?" "Ken?" Barbie thought she was dreaming, but no, there he was, Ken… here… in Paris! He leapt up onto the stage. "I would never break up with you," vowed Ken. "I promise you it was all a misunderstanding. The minute I found out, I knew I had to see you, but you had already left…" Just then he stopped and looked around him. "Did I show up at a bad time?" 'No, you showed up at the perfect time!" laughed Barbie. "And over here in Paris!"

The Flairies sprinkled their magic over Ken too, transforming his travel-worn suit into an ensemble just as cool and cutting-edge as Barbie's. Before they could talk any more, the man in the hotdog suit shouted up at the stage. "Unless you've got a huge pile of money for me, we're still tearing this place down in the morning!"

71

Everyone gasped. The Flairies were horrified at the reminder that their home and the source of their power would be no more in a matter of hours. Just when the dream seemed to be over, a guest put up her hand. "Amazing show!" she called. "I'd like to place an order for 10,000 pieces." Alice was astounded. "10,000 pieces? From this line?" "Absolument," nodded the guest. "I can write you a cheque immediatement." Barbie and Alice squealed with delight. "That would be lovely," beamed Millicent. "Please make the cheque out to the giant hotdog."

The Flairies' powers were safe! Realising her foolishness, Jacqueline apologised for everything she'd done, offering her congratulations to Millicent. Next Lilliana Roxelle stepped forward. "This is a Fashion Fairytale come true," she gushed. "I'd like to invite you to my black, white and pink party tonight. I'll send transportation." When Barbie and Ken stepped outside they were met by a gorgeous pink car. In an instant Glimmer had transformed it into a horse drawn carriage. "Your magic works when you transform things into something new," cried Shyne. "You're a designer too!"

There was one last surprise waiting for Barbie at the party. She was greeted by a member of the film production crew she'd been working with before her trip. "Thank the stars of Hollywood Boulevard I found you," cried the producer. Barbie gasped. "How did you know I was here?" "I saw your post for the fashion show and got here as fast as I could," the man explained. "The studio wants you back. They have a new movie that they really need you to work on… as director." The producer handed Barbie a script. "Will you consider it?" he begged. "I'll consider it," nodded Barbie. "But first, we all have some partying to do!"

The End

Postcard from Paris

At the start of the Fashion Fairytale movie, I couldn't help thinking about Ken and the friends that I'd left behind. I wrote lots of postcards home, but this one seems to have got smudged in the rain.

Can you help fill in the missing letters?
All the ones that have disappeared can be found in the word BARBIE.

D_ _ r T_r_sa,

So h_re I _m, in the f_sh_on c_pital of the wo_ld! I should _e h_ppy, _ut I c_n't stop thinking that I should be _usy f_lm_ng a movi_, not w_lking through the r_ _ ny P_r_s str_ _ ts! Aunt M_llic_nt's f_sh_on house is in trouble, but her n _ _ ce _l_ce and I are determined to put her _ _ ck on the d_s_gner map!

M_ss you alr_ _dy,

Barbie xxx

Millicent Maison

de Haute Couture

Paris

FRANCE

Designer
Dot-to-dot

Who does Sequin meet when I take her to Europe? Join up the dots to reveal Aunt Millicent's unforgettable Parisian pets!

Now unjumble the letters to reveal the animals' names.

CEUSQAJ _ _ _ _ _ _ _

IJINALAL _ _ _ _ _ _ _ _

Pretty Picture Quiz

I know that Alice will be a great designer one day! All it took was a few hours and a little bit of flairy sparkle for her to create a dazzling début collection. Take a close look at this snap of us working in the studio, then have a go at the quiz questions. Check your answers at the back of the book, then colour in an Eiffel Tower for every question that you got right.

1. Which pet has a pink ribbon in her hair?

....

2. How many windows does the studio have?

....

3. What colour cardigan is Alice wearing?

....

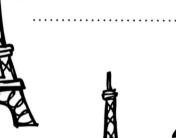

4. What is the pattern on the fabric that I'm holding?

....

5. How many mannequins are there in the studio?

....

Sparkle like a Fairy

Always ask a grown-up before mixing up your own beauty products!

For each pot you will need:
- An empty travel-sized make-up jar with a screw-on lid (old handcream tubs also work well)
- A tube of aloe vera gel
- Tubes of glitter in different colours
- Clean lolly stick
- White address labels
- Scissors
- Felt-tipped pens
- Pretty stickers

1. Squeeze some gel into your empty jar until it is about half full.

2. Choose a shade of glitter that you like, then tip a little into the empty jar.

3. Use the lolly stick to stir the glitter into the gel, adding a little at a time until you get the sparkle levels that you want.

4. Ask an adult to help you snip a white address label until it is the right size to fit on the top of the pot.

5. Use felt-tipped pens to fill in the label. Put it in place, then add some other pretty stickers for decoration. Now your glitter pot is ready to use!

A Fashion Fairytale
Colouring Poster

It was a magical moment when Shimmer, Shyne and Glimmer appeared on the catwalk at Millicent's new show. All the fashionistas gasped at the beauty of the gowns and the sparkle of the Flairies!

Use your favourite crayons or felt-tipped pens to bring this stunning scene to life...
When you've finished colouring, why not try outlining the Flairies with a silver pen or sprinkling some glitter over my lovely pink gown?

Crazy Quotes

Some of the lines from my Fashion Fairytale movie script seem to have got in a bit of a mix-up.

Get the scenes back on track by drawing lines to show who really said what.

A
'I don't need luck. I have talent. A talent for getting what I want.'

5 Ken

D
'And all we have to do is create an entire fashion line by tomorrow night!'

1 Aunt Millicent

3 Jacqueline

C
'People don't like my work anymore, it doesn't sell.'

4 Shimmer, Shyne & Glimmer

E
'A dog like Sequin... she makes me want to design again!'

B
'We have a flair that we share!'

6 Alice

F
'Remember, it's all for Barbie.'

2 Jacques

A Flair For Fashion

Do you have an eye for clothes? I'm going out to a glittering party tonight and I really can't decide what to wear. Please help me choose the outfit that will look the prettiest! Colour in a sparkle next to the outfit that suits me best

Design Time

Now I've been lucky enough to model Alice's stunning clothes, I'd love to design some unique new pieces for my friends. Would you like to do some sketches too? Before you start each one, think about the person you're designing for and ask yourselves some questions:

- What is their personality like?
- What type of clothes do they prefer to wear?
- What colours suit them best?

Got some ideas? Now it's time to get creative!

Alice's garments were totally original – I know yours will be too!

Summer shines on the tennis court, but she needs a little help with more glamorous occasions. Design a feminine prom dress that will match her beautiful blonde hair.

Headwear

Top

Bottom

Footwear

Raquelle

My supermodel friend looks good in anything! Push the boundaries by designing Raquelle a daring new cocktail dress that is sure to steal the show.

Headwear

Bottom

Top

Footwear

Nikki

Nikki so on-trend it hurts! Take my BFF back-to-basics by sketching a classic evening gown that she'll be able to treasure forever.

Headwear

Bottom

Top

Footwear

Now design a label to complete your fashion range as if it were a label on a haute couture garment...

Unique design by House of

. . . .

Pink Meringue Puffs

Sequin and I discovered these divine strawberry puffs in a quiet patisserie on a Parisian backstreet – they're our own special secret! When the shopkeeper offered to share the recipe I couldn't believe our luck. I wrote the recipe in my journal so that I could make a batch for my friends back home.

When you fancy a sweet treat, trying whipping up some puffs to share with your BFF. When they try one of these, you'll be the most popular girl on the block!

Ingredients

Before you start any recipe, check with a grown-up first.

To make 8 mouthwatering meringue puffs, you will need:

- 4 eggs
- Pinch of salt
- 300g caster sugar
- ½ teaspoon of vanilla extract

- Red food colouring
- Clotted cream
- A punnet of fresh strawberries

Recipe

1. Ask an adult to turn the oven onto 130°C/ 250°F/ Gas Mark 1.

2. Line two oven trays with non-stick baking paper so that they're completely covered.

3. Find two clean bowls, then gently crack open the first egg. Get a grown-up to help you carefully separate the white from the yolk, tipping the parts into the bowls. Repeat with the other three eggs.

4. Cover the egg yolks with plastic food wrap and pop them in the fridge. You won't need them for the meringue puffs, but you could save them for scrambled eggs and lots of other recipes.

5. Tip the egg whites into a mixing bowl then sprinkle over a pinch of salt. Whisk them up until they form soft glossy peaks.

6. Whisk in the caster sugar a little at a time, then use a spoon to stir in the vanilla extract. Slowly add a drop or two of red food colouring, stirring gently until the meringue is a beautiful shade of soft pink.

7. Place a large spoonful of meringue onto the first baking sheet, repeating all over both trays until the mixture is used up in even amounts. Make sure that you leave some space between each spoonful.

8. Cook the meringues for 30 minutes, then turn off the heat and let them cool with the oven door slightly open.

9. When the meringues are completely cooled, peel each one off its baking paper. Use a tablespoon of clotted cream to sandwich pairs of pink meringue together.

10. When all the meringues are paired up, arrange them on a cake stand with some sliced strawberries scattered on top. Sieve a little icing sugar over and your puffs are ready to serve!

Bursting with... Blooms

After I'd finished modelling Alice's fab fashions, I popped back to the studio to change. I couldn't believe my eyes when I walked in – someone had filled the room with beautiful rose bouquets! Could it have been the Flairies? Or perhaps it was Ken? Maybe I'll never know…

Can you count up how many bouquets are hiding in the studio? Write the number in here

FROM: Aunt Millicent

Look closely and you might even find who really did send the flowers after all! The bouquets were from

Lets Accessorise!

I've just blow-dried my hair and brushed it a hundred times. Now that my tresses are glossy and good to go, I need a few head-turning accessories! Can you help me jazz up my look by drawing some jewellery and hair decorations onto my picture?

There are some items on my dressing table that you might like to choose from...

Earrings, a diamond necklace, a fascinator, hair clips, a head band, combs, jewelled plaits, a tiara, fresh flowers or a velvet choker...

Barbie i can be... A Zoo Vet

It was time for the three trainee zoo vets to take action.

"Come on everybody!" cried Barbie. "Back to the trailer bikes!"

Nikki jumped on her's first. "We've got to be quick!"

The girls sped along the bumpy track to feed the hamsters and guinea pigs. Teresa and Nikki quickly leapt off their bikes with some dried nuts and seeds, plus a handful of fresh fruit food. The little furry creatures were soon nibbling on a delicious supper!

"Go team!" cheered Barbie, ticking the little animals off her list.

When they reached the kangaroo enclosure, Barbie raced over to deliver their meal.

"Where next?" asked Teresa.

"Toucans, parrots and penguins," said Barbie. "Let's hit the road!"

The BFF pedalled as fast they could, taking care to avoid the visitors strolling through the zoo. As soon as the girls arrived in the bird enclosure, a flock of colourful parrots swooped down from the trees.

"Look," gasped Barbie. "They're eating out of my hands!"

Once all the tropical birds were fed, the girls arrived at the zoo's ice dome.
The hungry penguins waddled over, keen to get some fish.
   "Brrrr! It's chilly in here," said Barbie, as the trio carefully stepped onto the slippery ice.
"We should have brought ice-skates!" giggled Nikki.
   Suddenly Teresa lost her balance, sliding onto the floor with a bump! Barbie
and Nikki put down their buckets and helped her up.

"I've got an idea!" said Barbie. "Let's hold hands to help each other
balance on the slippery rocks."
   In a few moments, the three girls were moving steadily over the rocks.
They made their way to the penguins and then tossed them some silvery fish.
The little creatures squawked with happiness, swallowing each one whole.
   "I wish we could stay and watch," sighed Nikki.
"Me too," said Barbie. "But we still haven't finished the list!"

"The baby pandas are next," said Barbie. "I hope it's warmer where they live!"
The girls got back on their bikes and followed the signs for the bear enclosures. Teresa carefully unlocked the baby panda area, while Nikki and Barbie followed behind with bottles of milk. At first they couldn't spot a single bear – the shy little things had hidden in the bamboo!
"It's OK, little pandas," whispered Barbie. "We've brought your supper."

The girls held out the bottles and waited patiently. The tiny pandas peeped out at them.
"There's no need to be shy," whispered Teresa. "We won't hurt you."
The fluffy little creatures slowly crept towards them and began drinking their bottles. When they'd finished all their milk each one began to yawn.
"I think it's time for their nap," smiled Nikki.
"Sweet dreams, pandas!" whispered Barbie, as the girls tiptoed back to their bikes.
Teresa couldn't resist one more cuddle.
"They are so adorable," she cooed. "I wish I could take them all home!"

The next location on Barbie's list was Wild Bird Lake. The girls freewheeled round to the water's edge, parking their bikes underneath a pretty willow tree.

"Oh Barbie," cried Teresa. "Look!"

The three girls gasped in delight. The birds were the most beautiful creatures they'd ever seen! Peacocks, cockatoos and parakeets all gathered around them, each more colourful than the last.

"Those pink flamingos are stunning," smiled Nikki, scattering their seeds.

Suddenly, a group of birds began flapping their wings down by the water.

"I wonder what's happening over there?" said Barbie.

Teresa and Nikki followed Barbie as she made her way over to the excited birds.

"Look!" cried Barbie. "They're watching an egg hatch."

Just at that moment, the egg on the ground wobbled and two little feet popped out! The girls smiled as a tiny flamingo chick tapped out of the shell and chirped at his mum.

"Isn't he sweet?" sighed Nikki.

"Let's leave him with his mum while we feed the other birds," said Barbie.

When they'd finished scattering the last few handfuls of food, Barbie pulled the list out of her pocket.

"Let's see what's next," she said, as Teresa and Nikki leaned in too.

"There's nothing else to do," Nikki laughed. "Everything's been ticked."

"We've fed all the animals in the zoo," nodded Barbie. "Nice teamwork, guys!" Suddenly, Barbie spotted the vet walking over to meet them. When they told her they'd finished their rounds, she was very impressed!

"We spent too much time playing with the animals at first," Barbie explained.

"But then we stuck to the list and worked our way through."

"You've done a great job!" smiled the vet. "Well done, girls! All the animals and birds are happy and fed. That's thanks to you! You girls could all make great zoo vets." For Barbie and her friends the compliment was thanks enough, but the grateful vet generously gave the delighted trio free passes to come back any time.

"Now you'll be able to visit the zoo animals you've helped care for," smiled the vet. Barbie gave Teresa and Nikki a hug.

"Awesome!" she cried. "What a brilliant day."

When Isabella and Anna had finished making up their story, they put down their dolls and went over to see Anna's bunnies. There was a mummy rabbit and two adorable babies.

All of them had fluffy white fur and the cutest apricot patches!

"Let's be vets just like Barbie," said Isabella. "I'll top up the bunnies' water bottle," said Anna, lifting the cage door so she could carefully fill it up.

"And I'll feed them some crunchy carrots!" smiled Isabella, picking up a soft white bunny and cradling it to her chest.

The girls both grinned – being a vet really was the best fun ever!

The End

Animal Anagrams

Nikki, Teresa and I met some amazing animals in the zoo vet story! Can you imagine what it would be like to bottle-feed a fluffy baby panda or hold a tiny newborn deer in your arms? I've made a list of the most adorable creatures that we came across – put the letters in the right order to spell out each one.

1. BERAZ
_ _ _ _ _

2. EATHLENP
_ _ _ _ _ _ _ _

3. RATORP
_ _ _ _ _ _

4. HOLDNIP
_ _ _ _ _ _ _

5. NEPUNIG
_ _ _ _ _ _ _

6. GANLIMOF
_ _ _ _ _ _ _ _

7. LOAAK
_ _ _ _ _

8. RIFAGEF
_ _ _ _ _ _ _

The day begins! ....
....

Nikki's Story Scrapbook

When Nikki's having fun she can't stop snapping! During our day at the zoo she took tons of photos with her digital camera — she even passed the gadget to visitors so that she could be in some of the shots too! I've printed out my favourite ones and stuck them in this scrapbook. Write captions underneath each photo so that we can remember the day forever.

....
....

....
....

The Pet Set

Sequin

Lacey

Sequin travels everywhere with me! She's sweet-natured, friendly and perfectly behaved, whether she's trotting round the shops or running along the beach with the wind in her fur. I call her my 'diamond in the ruff', because when I found her she was lost and lonely with patches of mud all over her pretty white coat. When I took her home and cleaned her up, I discovered a stunning show poodle hiding underneath! Now that we've found each other, Sequin will never be homeless again.

This year I had the most amazing birthday present from my friends – a darling little Chihuahua called Lacey! Lacey is only dinky, but she's got bags and bags of energy. Being a pup, she needs lots of extra care and attention. I feed her three times a day and take her to puppy training classes too. Sometimes she can be a little naughty. Once I caught her chewing my best pink shoes instead of her toy bone! I don't mind a bit, with a bit of help from Sequin she'll grow into a delightful doggy.

Pet Puzzle:
What type of dog is Sequin?

....

Pet Puzzle:
How often does a pup like Lacey need to be fed?

....

Have you met my gorgeous, glamorous pets? Each one of them means the world to me, filling my day with smiles! Even when I'm working on a busy shoot, I always make sure that I'm back in time to give each one a cuddle and some special attention.

Looking after pets is hard work, but worth every wonderful second!

Blissa

Tawny

Have you ever seen a kitten that's fluffier than Blissa? My adorable longhaired pussycat makes me purr with happiness every time I pick her up. I share Blissa with my sisters Kelly and Stacie, and we all take turns looking after her. There's lots to do – every day Blissa needs grooming, feeding and a fresh litter tray. Blissa thanks us with lots of cuddles. She's a true fashionista too! She loves dressing in sparkly kitty accessories and her favourite colour is pink, just like me!

I've had Tawny every since she was a golden baby foal! Now that she's all grown up, she has a colt of her own. Tawny is a very special pet because I've had her such a long time. She taught me to ride and showed me how horses like to be looked after. Tawny and her colt live in a meadow beside my house, but if I have to go out of town I take them to stay at her favourite stables. That way I know that my gorgeous pair are getting star treatment 24/7!

Pet Puzzle:
Can you think of three things that a kitten needs?

....

Pet Puzzle:
What is the name of a baby horse?

....

Poptastic Colours!

Next time it's raining outside, pull on some layers in the brightest colours you can find! It's impossible to wear sky blues, golden yellows and stunning pinks without feeling happy! Can you help Teresa and I put together outfits in our favourite rainbow shades?

Colour-by-numbers, using the key below as guide.

1 = 💜 Barbie pink
2 = 🖤 vibrant purple
3 = 🩵 true blue
4 = 💙 ocean turquoise
5 = 🤍 sunrise yellow
6 = ❤️ ruby red

Rock Wrong?

I love playing in my band! Sometimes on a Friday night we do a set in the high school common room. Rocking out with all of our friends is the biggest buzz ever! To get a front row view of the stage, put this photo of me in the correct order.

There's a word hidden in the picture too.

1 ... **r**

2 ... **p**

3 ... **t**

4 ... **y**

5 ... **a**

The correct order should be _ _ _ _ _
Find the hidden word then write it into the phrase below.

Let's rock this _ _ _ _ _!

Mystery Mall Trip

Would you like to play a fun guessing game with me? I'm off to the mall to buy a birthday gift for someone special today, but I'm keeping their ID under wraps! Look at the names in the frame, then use the clues to help you discover the friend that I'm going shopping for.

Nikki

Ken

Teresa

Ryan

Kelly

Raquelle

Summer

Steven

Stacie

Clues...

1. The mystery person has dark hair.

2. They have brown eyes.

3. They are female

The person is

....

Write on!

Have you got a penpal? When Teresa and I have to travel on acting and modelling assignments we keep in touch by post! Every time I spot my BFF's familiar handwriting on an envelope I know there'll be a ton of news and girlie gossip inside. Emails and instant messaging is great, but nothing beats the fun of writing and receiving a proper letter. It's time to get scribbling…

♥ Fill your letters with news about your friends, school and holidays. Try and describe you and your world so that the other person really feels they are getting to know what makes you tick.

♥ Don't be fooled into thinking that your messages have to be over-long. A postcard, notelet or hand-drawn picture are just as exciting to receive through the mail.

♥ Keep your letters as regular as you can, even if it's only once a month.

♥ Pop a little surprise into the envelopes from time to time. A photo, pressed flower or some stickers will make your pal's day.

♥ Don't forget to ask about your friend too! Include some questions, so that you don't miss out on all their exciting news.

The Write Way

Before you share addresses with anybody or agree to be a pen friend, always check with the grown-ups in you house first.

Here are three ideas on how to find a writing buddy...

1. Ask your teacher to enroll your class in a pen pal scheme. With these schemes your entire year group can be put in touch with children the same age as you living on the other side of the world.

2. If you have a good friend that's moving away, ask if they'd like to stay in touch by post! It will make their move much easier if you both promise to keep in touch.

3. Do you have a cousin or relative that you don't get to see as often as you'd like? Suggest that they start swapping letters and cards with you.

High School
Hide and Seek

When we're not in class or the library, my friends love chillaxing in the student common room! Our high school is so much fun, there's always music playing or some hot news buzzing round the gang. Why not come and join us?

Today we're playing a cool game of hide and seek. Look around the room, answering the questions that you come across.

Colour in a pretty pink 'Barbie' icon for every one you complete.

What instrument is Ryan playing?

How many tea cups can you see in the café area?

Who's standing at the side of the stage? *Barbie*

Point to girl with funky pink necktie. *Barbie*

What's the weather like outside?

How many pink chairs can you count?

Find the cakes in the kitchen area. *Barbie*

What colour is Ken's sweater?

How many people are wearing blue jeans? *Barbie*

Fab Frock! Fab Friends!

From the minute I did up the satin sash, I knew I was going to love this heavenly new ballgown. The swishy skirts are so me!

Shall we make a keepsake portrait of you and I dressed in our favourite things? Draw a picture of yourself into the frame wearing your most fabulous dress. Now colour us both in.

Barbie and ....

Best Friends Forever

Make a Crystal Snowflake card

This greeting card is sparkly and delightful. You could send it as a Christmas card or give it to a special friend with a winter birthday.

For one card you will need:

- A blank folded card in a bright colour
- A large mug
- Several teaspoons of table salt
- Pencil
- Thin black card
- Scissors
- Paintbrush
- Paper glue

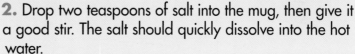

SAFETY FIRST!
This craft activity uses very hot water! Ask a grown-up to help you so that no one gets burned.

1. Boil some water in the kettle then ask an adult to pour some into a large drinking mug.

2. Drop two teaspoons of salt into the mug, then give it a good stir. The salt should quickly dissolve into the hot water.

3. Keep adding spoonfuls of salt, stirring them in each time. When the salt starts floating in the mixture and no more can be dissolved, put the mug to one side.

4. Draw a snowflake design on the black card, taking care to make it small enough to fit on the front of the greetings card. Carefully cut the design out and lay it on some old newspaper.

5. Use a brush to paint the snowflake all over with the salt solution. Push your brush right down to the bottom of the mug so that it gets covered in salt crystals with every stroke.

6. Leave your snowflake overnight. When the salt has completely dried out, stick it on the front of your greetings card. Add a message in a sparkly pen and your beautiful crystal card is ready to send!

Shoe Heaven

There are so many shoes in my closet, sometimes it's hard to know which pair to choose! Colour in this picture, shading your favourite heels in a vibrant shade of pink. I know I can count on you to choose something stunning.

New Year's Promises

Thank you so much sharing for my Winter Annual, I hope you've had fun! Now that we're best friends, there's just time for me to tell you about my New Year's resolutions.

A resolution is another word for the promises people make on December 31 as they look towards the year ahead. Read my six special promises then colour in a heart next to the ones you would like to keep too.

I promise to see my friends lots and lots.

I promise to have a pampering session with my BFF.

I promise to learn a new dance routine.

I promise to try a new sport.

I promise to make a new recipe.

I promise to wear lots of gorgeous pink clothes!

Do you have a resolution of your own? Write it in here, then keep this Annual in a special place so that you never forget it.

....

....

Answers

Page 26 – Kitty Crèche

Barbie is holding 2 kittens and there are 5 hiding.

Page 28 – Late Date Maze

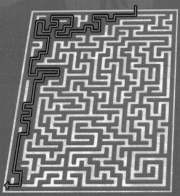

Page 29 – Superstar Sisters

Page 30 – Musical Moves Wordsearch

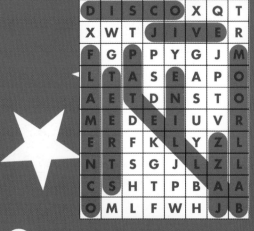

Page 34 – Perfect Pairs

Page 44 – Pit Stop Problem

Page 45 – Cheerleading Crossword

Page 46 – My Secret Diary

Dear Diary, What a busy day it has been! I was woken up first thing by the sound of the phone ringing. It was Teresa calling to say that the sun was shining! She asked if the whole gang could come over to my house for a swim in the pool, so of course I said yes!
Steven and Ken arrived first, closely followed by Nikki, Ryan and Raquelle. Teresa came last armed with a big box of her homemade cupcakes.
We had so many laughs playing in the pool. When we couldn't splash anymore, we hung out eating cupcakes.
At three, Ken turned my flatscreen TV on just in time to watch Summer win her tennis tournament!
After everyone had left, I chilled out in my bedroom with Sequin and Lacey. What a lucky girl I am to be Barbie!

Page 47 – Shopping Surprises

Page 52 – Mystery Meeting!

```
F R O S T
C R Y S T A L S
  I C E S K A T E S
G L O V E S
    R E I N D E E R
    S N O W F L A K E
```

Page 74 – Postcard from Paris

Dear Teresa,
So here I am, in the fashion capital of the world!
I should be happy, but I can't stop thinking that I should
be busy filming a movie, not walking through the rainy
Paris streets! Aunt Millicent's fashion house is in trouble,
but her niece Alice and I are determined to put her back
on the designer map!
Miss you already, Barbie xxx

Page 75 – Designer Dot-to-dot
JACQUES & JILLIANA.

Page 76 – Pretty Picture Quiz
1–Sequin, 2–Four, 3–Lilac,
4–Polka dot, 5–Three

Page 80 – Crazy Quotes
1–C, 2–E, 3–A, 4–B, 5–F, 6–D

Page 86 – Bursting with Blooms
There were 7 bouquets. They were
sent by Aunt Millicent.

Page 94 – Animal Anagrams
1–ZEBRA, 2–ELEPHANT, 3–PARROT,
4–DOLPHIN, 5–PENGUIN,
6–FLAMINGO, 7–KOALA, 8–GIRAFFE

Pages 96 – The Pet Set
• Sequin is a poodle.
• Lacey needs feeding 3 times a day.
• Blissa needs grooming, to be fed
  regularly and her litter tray changed.
• A baby horse is called a foal.

Page 99 – Rock Wrong?

Let's rock this party!

Page 100 – Mystery Mall Trip
The person is Nikki.

Pages 102 – High School Hide and Seek
Ryan is playing guitar.
There are five tea cups in the café.
Raquelle is at the side of the stage.
It's a sunny Malibu day
outside.
There are six pink
chairs in the scene.
Ken's sweater is
purple.
Two people are
wearing blue jeans.